Geography: The World and Its People

Vocabulary Activities

GLENCOE
McGraw-Hill

New York, New York   Columbus, Ohio   Mission Hills, California   Peoria, Illinois

To The Teacher

Geography: The World and Its People Vocabulary Activities helps students to master unfamiliar words and terms used in the student edition. The worksheets emphasize identification of word meanings and provide visual and kinesthetic reinforcement of language skills. Vocabulary practice typically involves matching activities, sentence completion, and word puzzles. These worksheets are intended for use by students of all ability levels.

Customize Your Resources

No matter how you organize your teaching resources, Glencoe has what you need.

The **Teacher's Classroom Resources** for *Geography: The World and Its People* provides you with a wide variety of supplemental materials to enhance the classroom experience. These resources appear as individual booklets in a carryall tote box. The booklets are designed to open flat so that pages can be easily photocopied without removing them from their booklet. However, if you choose to create separate files, the pages are perforated for easy removal. You may customize these materials using our file folders or tabbed dividers.

The individual booklets and the file management kit supplied in **Teacher's Classroom Resources** give you the flexibility to organize these resources in a combination that best suits your teaching style. Below are several alternatives:

- **Organize all resources by category**
  (all tests, all geography themes activities, all cooperative learning activities, etc., filed separately)
- **Organize all resources by category and chapter**
  (all Chapter 1 activities, all Chapter 1 tests, etc.)
- **Organize resources sequentially by lesson**
  (activities, quizzes, readings, etc., for Chapter 1, Chapter 2, and so on)

Send all inquiries to:
Glencoe/McGraw-Hill
936 Eastwind Drive
Westerville, Ohio 43081

ISBN 0-02-823712-9

Printed in the United States of America.

2 3 4 5 6 7 8 9 10 11 12   MAL   02 01 00 99 98 97 96

Vocabulary Activities

vo•cab•u•lar•y vo-'kab-y
1: a list or collection of wo
alphabetically arranged

Table of Contents

CHAPTER **1** Vocabulary Activity

vo•cab•u•lar•y vo-'kab-y
1: a list or collection of wor
alphabetically arranged

Looking at the Earth: Words to Know

DIRECTIONS: Definitions Select the terms that complete each numbered item below. On a second sheet of paper, write the correct terms next to the number of the statements.

geography	earthquake	landform	galaxy
latitude	erosion	crust	revolution
relative location	peninsula	plate tectonics	solstice
movement	absolute location	tsunami	core
solar system	longitude	plateau	magma
leap year	place	strait	fault
equinox	region	hemisphere	weathering
mantle	orbit	grid system	isthmus
continent	axis	environment	atmosphere

1. Six terms that name or help describe the five themes of geography.

2. Four terms that help define absolute location.

3. Two terms that name large systems in the universe.

4. Four words that name parts of, or something found in, the inner Earth.

5. Five words that name land or land features on Earth.

6. One word that names a water feature.

7. Four terms that relate to the theory of moving plates and what the plates can cause.

8. Five words that are needed to explain why Earth has seasons and when seasons change.

9. One term for the time period that makes the calendar year equal to the actual time it takes Earth to revolve around the sun.

10. Two words that name effects of wind, water, chemicals, or ice on land.

11. One word that names something that surrounds Earth and supports life.

12. One word that relates to *all* of the previous words.

CHAPTER 2 Vocabulary Activity

vo•cab•u•lar•y vo-'kab-y
1: a list or collection of wo
alphabetically arranged

Water, Climate, and Vegetation: Words to Know

DIRECTIONS: Fill in the Blanks Select a term from below to complete each of the sentences.

> Mediterranean climate   evaporation   current   climate
> marine west coast climate   tropics   rain forest   savanna
> humid subtropical climate   water vapor   condensation   aquifer
> humid continental climate   water cycle   precipitation   weather
> groundwater

1. In the _____, the region near the Equator, you may find a lush

_____ of tall trees with canopies that block the sun or a drier grassland area called

a _____ .

2. The Gulf Stream is a warm water _____ .

3. Mid-latitude climates include two coastal climates, _____ _____

_____ _____ and _____ _____ , as

well as the inland _____ _____ _____ and the

_____ _____ _____ , found near the tropics.

4. The constant movement of water, a process known as the _____ , can be

broken into steps: first, _____ of water occurs, and liquid water changes into

_____ _____ . In high, cool air, _____ of water vapor occurs,

and clouds are formed. _____ , such as rain, snow, or sleet, falls back to Earth.

5. Under Earth's surface, _____ can accumulate in an _____ ,
a rock layer with flowing water.

6. _____ is what a day is like outside, but _____ is what most days are like
this time of year.

DIRECTIONS: Writing Sentences Use each of the following terms correctly
in a complete sentence. Write the sentences on a separate sheet of paper.

> vegetation   hurricane   typhoon   rain shadow   permafrost
> timberline   monsoon   tundra   elevation   steppe

Copyright © by Glencoe/McGraw-Hill.

CHAPTER 3 Vocabulary Activity

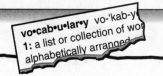

The World's People: Words to Know

DIRECTIONS: Matching Select the term that matches each definition below. Write the correct term in the space provided.

nonrenewable resource	cultural diffusion	emigrate	socialism
renewable resource	natural resource	literacy rate	civilization
standard of living	free enterprise	culture	
population density	language family	refugee	

1. A group of related languages _____ _____

2. An economic system in which business people face little government control _____ _____

3. A measure of a people's quality of living based on their income and possessions _____

4. The opposite of immigrate, or enter a country _____

5. A measure of the percentage of people who can read and write _____ _____

6. The average number of people living in a given area _____ _____

7. A group of people sharing a way of living, beliefs, and traditions _____

8. A person forced to flee his or her own country _____

9. A highly advanced culture _____

10. A resource that cannot be replaced _____ _____

11. An economic system controlled by the government _____

12. A resource that can be replaced if used wisely _____ _____

13. The process by which cultures share knowledge and skills _____ _____

14. Something taken from nature that people use to meet needs _____ _____

DIRECTIONS: Writing Sentences Use each of the following terms correctly in a complete sentence. Write the sentences on a separate sheet of paper.

developed country	urbanization	demographer	fossil fuel
hydroelectric power	birthrate	pollution	pesticide
subsistence farming	solar energy	death rate	acid rain
developing country	service industry	famine	

CHAPTER 4 Vocabulary Activity

vo•cab•u•lar•y vo-'kab-y
1: a list or collection of wo
alphabetically arranged

The United States: Words to Know

DIRECTIONS: Crossword Puzzle Complete the crossword puzzle by spelling out the terms called for in the clues.

free enterprise system   contiguous   ethnic group   colony
interdependent   dry farming   immigrant   urban
service industry   revolution   acid rain   coral reef
national park   multicultural   rural   republic
megalopolis   farm belt   mobile

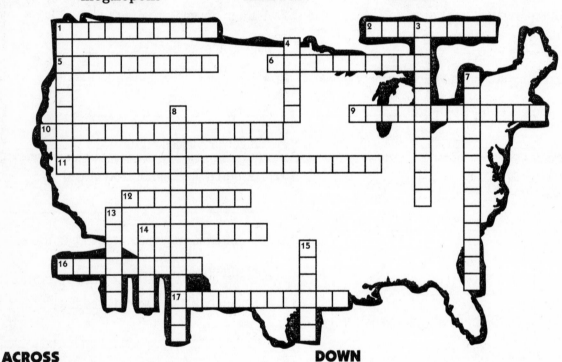

ACROSS

1. joined inside a common boundary
2. region with many productive farms
5. a sudden political change
6. way of plowing land to hold rainwater
9. land set aside by the government for recreation and preservation
10. industry not producing a product
11. system in which people run businesses with limited government control
12. air pollution that mixes with rain
14. government in which people elect officials
16. person who comes to live in a new land
17. people who share a common culture

DOWN

1. submerged or low-lying ocean structure formed from skeletons of small sea animals
3. super city
4. densely populated
7. having many different cultures
8. reliant on each other
13. moving from place to place
14. sparsely populated
15. overseas settlement tied to parent country

CHAPTER 5 Vocabulary Activity

vo•cab•u•lar•y vo-'kab-y
1: a list or collection of wor
alphabetically arranged

Canada: Words to Know

DIRECTIONS: Word Puzzle The alphabetical list contains the letters for spelling the terms that answer the questions below. Write the term to answer each question, and cross out the letters used to spell the term. After you complete the first seven questions, you will have used all but five letters. Use the five extra letters to complete question 8.

prairie
cordillera
fossil fuel
newsprint

bilingual
prime minister
parliamentary democracy

AAAAAAAAABCCCDDEEEEEEEFFFG
IIIIIIIIIILLLLLLMMMMNNNNNNOOOPPPP
RRRRRRRRRSSSSTTTTUUWYY

1. Reserves of oil and natural gas were discovered in Canada's Prairie Provinces. What type of fuel is oil or natural gas? _____

2. In this system of government, used in the United Kingdom and Canada, voters elect representatives to parliament. What is this system of government called? _____

3. Today, many people speak two languages fluently. What term could describe such people?

_____

4. Picture an area of rolling grasslands with rich soil. There are many names for this type of land. What is this type of land called in Canada and the United States? _____

5. This person is the leader of the largest political party in Canada's Parliament, and Canada's leader. What is the leader called? _____

6. Mountain ranges can run side by side. What is such an area of ranges called? _____

7. A particular kind of paper is made into newspapers. What is the paper called? _____

8. The five extra letters can be reordered to form the abbreviation of a trade agreement approved by Canada, the United States, and Mexico. Write the letters in the correct order.

____ ____ ____ ____ ____

CHAPTER **6** Vocabulary Activity

vo•cab•u•lar•y vo-'kab-y
1: a list or collection of wo
alphabetically arranged

Mexico: Words to Know

DIRECTIONS: Answering Questions Select a term to answer each question below. Write the term in the blank.

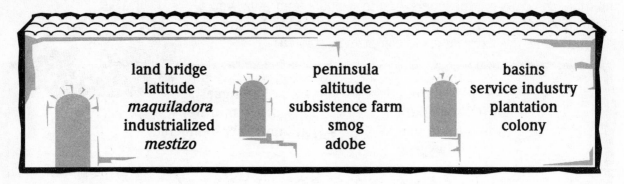

land bridge
latitude
maquiladora
industrialized
mestizo

peninsula
altitude
subsistence farm
smog
adobe

basins
service industry
plantation
colony

1. What landform is surrounded by water on three sides? _____

2. What kind of farm provides enough food for one family? _____

3. What word names a person of mixed Native American and European background? _____

4. What is an industry that helps people but does not produce goods? _____

5. What is the pollutant formed from smoke and fog? _____

6. What is a large farm that produces a crop for sale? _____

7. What word means "elevation"? _____

8. What landform links two larger landmasses? _____

9. What is the name for a factory in Mexico where goods from other countries are put together?

_____

10. What word describes a country or region that has many businesses and factories? _____

11. What word is a building material used long ago and today? _____

12. What term tells how far north or south of the Equator a place lies? _____

13. What words means broad, flat valleys? _____

14. What is a name for an overseas territory? _____

CHAPTER 7 Vocabulary Activity

vo•cab•u•lar•y vo-'kab-y
1: a list or collection of wo
alphabetically arranged

Central America and the West Indies: Words to Know

DIRECTIONS: Fill in the Blanks Select one of the following terms to complete each of the sentences below.

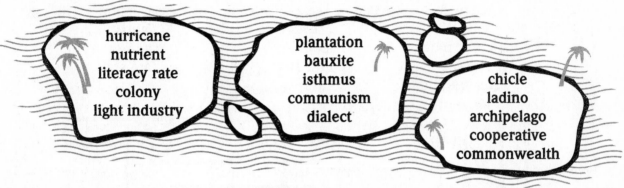

hurricane
nutrient
literacy rate
colony
light industry

plantation
bauxite
isthmus
communism
dialect

chicle
ladino
archipelago
cooperative
commonwealth

1. Workers mine _____ for export to factories that make aluminum.

2. A high _____ reveals that most of a country's people can read.

3. In Cuba, under the system of government called _____ , farmers may work on

a government run _____ .

4. A strong _____ ripped through the islands, uprooting trees and flooding highways.

5. Crops grown on a large _____ may include tobacco, sugarcane, coffee, and bananas to sell.

6. A mineral supplying food to plants is called a _____ .

7. Rain forest workers gather _____ for making chewing gum.

8. A _____ is a Guatemalan who speaks Spanish and follows European ways.

9. In 1952 Puerto Rico became a _____ , or partly self-ruling territory; in earlier

times, it had been a _____ of Spain.

10. From the thin _____ , bordered on each side by a glistening ocean, we could

see some of the islands in the _____ .

11. The woman spoke a _____ that sounded rhythmic.

12. A _____ may produce food products, cigars, or household goods.

CHAPTER 8 Vocabulary Activity

vo•cab•u•lar•y vo-'kab-y
1: a list or collection of wor
alphabetically arranged

Brazil and Its Neighbors: Words to Know

DIRECTIONS: Crossword Puzzle Complete the crossword puzzle by spelling out the terms called for in the clues.

basin	*selva*	escarpment
sisal	*favela*	*llanos*
hydroelectric power	altitude	*caudillo*
landlocked	buffer state	welfare state
gaucho	cassava	

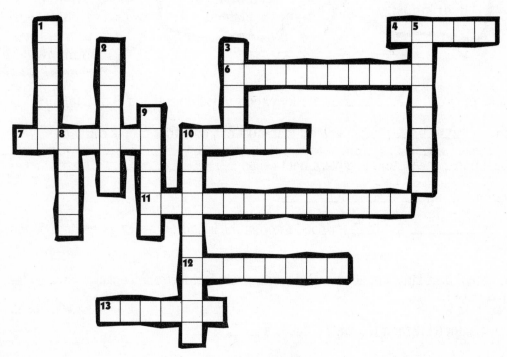

ACROSS

4. a broad, flat plain surrounded by higher land
6. a steep cliff
7. a plant whose roots are used to make food
10. name for the region of plains in northern South America
11. power made from running water: _____ power
12. harsh ruler of Venezuela in 1800s and 1900s
13. small country between two larger powers: _____ state

DOWN

1. area of poor housing in a Brazilian city
2. state that uses tax money to help people: _____ state
3. Brazilian word for tropical rain forest
5. elevation, or height of land
8. a plant material used for making rope
9. a ranch hand or cowhand
10. word to describe a country with no seacoast

CHAPTER **9** Vocabulary Activity

vo•cab•u•lar•y vo-'kab-y
1: a list or collection of wor
alphabetically arranged

The Andean Countries: Words to Know

DIRECTIONS: Fill in the Blanks Write a term from the box in each blank in the paragraphs below.

cordillera	*llanos*	**cash crop**
campesinos	*altiplano*	**navigable**
empire	*quinoa*	**sodium nitrate**
tannin	*estancia*	*gaucho*

In rural Colombia, farmers called (**1**)_____ grow food mostly for their families. Another

Colombian farmer might work on a plantation growing a (**2**)_____ , such as coffee. In

Bolivia, a farmer plants hardy crops, such as potatoes and (**3**)_____ , a grain. Many rural

farmers have no chemical fertilizers, made with (**4**)_____ , to enrich poor soil.

My family lives in Colombia on plains we call the (**5**)_____ . I have traveled to the

Andes and seen the (**6**)_____ —the ranges standing in great, long lines. Now, I want

to go to Argentina. Like my grandfather, I'll work on a huge ranch, or (**7**)_____ , on

the Pampas. I will be a (**8**)_____ , tending the herds. The ranch will send beef to

market and hides to the factory to be prepared, with (**9**)_____ . I will buy

black leather boots and a belt.

With her guides, Mercha crossed the mountains and reached the high and level

(**10**)_____ , where Lake Titicaca lies. This lake, used for transport for centuries, is the

highest (**11**)_____ lake in the world. As Mercha stared at the lake, she won-

dered if a great (**12**)_____ , like that of the Inca, had existed here long ago.

CHAPTER 10 Vocabulary Activity

vo•cab•u•lar•y vo-'kab-y
1: a list or collection of wor
alphabetically arranged

The British Isles and Scandinavia: Words to Know

DIRECTIONS: Matching Select a term that fits each set of clues below. Write the correct term in the space provided.

moor	constitutional monarchy	fjord
loch	peat	welfare state
parliamentary democracy	bog	geyser

1. This is found in Scotland. It is a long, narrow bay surrounded by high mountains.

_____

2. This is found in the United Kingdom. It is a form of government in which voters elect representatives to Parliament. _____

3. This is found in Ireland. It is wet ground with decaying plants that can be used as a fuel.

_____

4. This is found in the United Kingdom. It is a region of windy highlands without trees.

_____

5. This is found in Sweden, Denmark, and Finland. It is a government that uses tax money to provide educational, medical, and other services for citizens. _____

6. This is found in Ireland. It is low swampy land. _____

7. This is found in Iceland. It is caused by heat underground. It is hot water and steam bursting to the surface. _____

8. This is found in the United Kingdom, Sweden, Norway, and Denmark. It is a form of government in which a monarch represents the people but does not rule. _____

9. This is found in Norway. It is like one kind of Scottish loch. It is a steep-sided valley of seawater.

_____

CHAPTER 11 Vocabulary Activity

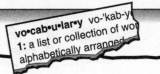

Northwestern Europe: Words to Know

DIRECTIONS: Word Puzzle Fill in the puzzle by spelling out the terms called for in the first 11 clues. Then complete term 12, spelled vertically, and write its definition on line 12.

navigable   loess   polder
republic   *autobahn*   multinational firm
communism   dialect   neutrality
acid rain   Holocaust   watershed

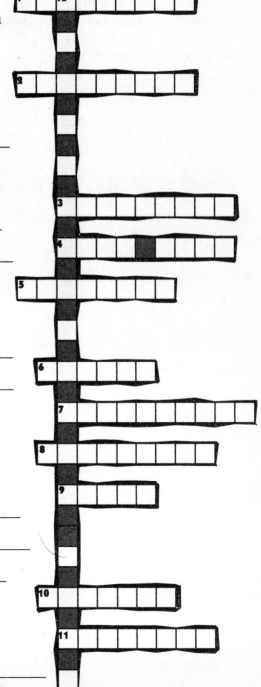

1. a government, usually under one strong leader, that controls the economy and the people

_____

2. the organized killing of six million European Jews and six million other people during World War II

_____

3. able to be used by large ships _____

4. rainfall that holds chemical pollution and can

harm plants _____

5. superhighway in Germany _____

6. an area of land reclaimed from the sea _____

7. not taking of sides in disagreements and wars

between countries _____

8. a high place from which rivers flow in

different directions _____

9. fertile soil deposited by the wind _____

10. a local form of a language _____

11. a government in which people elect

government officials _____

12. _____

Copyright © by Glencoe/McGraw-Hill.

Name_____ Date _____ Class _____

CHAPTER 12 Vocabulary Activity

vo•cab•u•lar•y vo-'kab-y
1: a list or collection of wo
alphabetically arranged

Southern Europe: Words to Know

DIRECTIONS: Matching Select a term that matches each definition. Write the correct term in the space provided.

plateau   city-state   suburb
textile   mainland   emigrate
dialect   elevation
sirocco   service industry

1. *Definition:* an industry that does not make goods but provides a service

   Term: _____ _____

2. *Definition:* a modern area that surrounds or is next to a city center

   Term: _____

3. *Definition:* land that is part of another large landmass

   Term: _____

4. *Definition:* move from one country to settle in another country

   Term: _____

5. *Definition:* height above sea level

   Term: _____

6. *Definition:* hot dry winds blowing from North Africa

   Term: _____

7. *Definition:* ancient city with an independent government that rules the countryside around it

   Term: _____ _____

8. *Definition:* form of a language that is local to a region

   Term: _____

9. *Definition:* a flat landmass higher than the surrounding land

   Term: _____

10. *Definition:* having to do with cloth or the clothing industry

   Term: _____

CHAPTER **13** Vocabulary Activity

vo•cab•u•lar•y vo-'kab-y
1: a list or collection of wo
alphabetically arranged

Eastern Europe: Words to Know

DIRECTIONS: Fill in the Blanks Select a term from below to fill each blank in the following paragraphs.

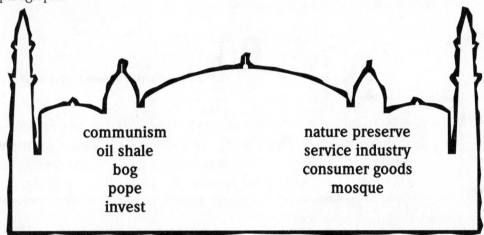

communism
oil shale
bog
pope
invest

nature preserve
service industry
consumer goods
mosque

In the system of government known as (**1**) _____, a country's economy is controlled by the government. After the fall of communism in Europe, countries began developing free enterprise systems. Factories turned from heavy industry to the manufacturing of (**2**) _____ _____, such as clothing, furniture, and household items. Recognizing the value of a (**3**) _____ _____, individuals set up, for example, repair shops and tourist guide services.

World religions have different names for similar things. Protestants, for example, worship in a church, whereas Muslims worship in a (**4**) _____. Tibetan Buddhists may look to the Dalai Lama as their highest priest, while Catholics see the (**5**) _____ as their highest religious leader.

To (**6**) _____ is to commit money to a business to gain a later profit. But people also invest in the environment. In this case, investing may mean stopping pollution or setting up a protected area, such as a (**7**) _____ _____.

Long ago, much of Earth may have been a swampy (**8**) _____ . Over millions of years, plants grew, died, were buried and decayed. With heat and pressure, they turned to oil. Today, the oil may fill rocks, forming rich deposits of (**9**) _____ _____.

CHAPTER 14 Vocabulary Activity

vo•cab•u•lar•y vo-'kab-y
1: a list or collection of wor
alphabetically arranged

Russia: Words to Know

DIRECTIONS: Fill in the Blanks Write a term from the box in each blank in the
sentences below. The sentences suggest some opposites.

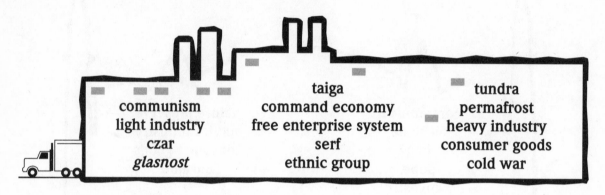

communism
light industry
czar
glasnost

taiga
command economy
free enterprise system
serf
ethnic group

tundra
permafrost
heavy industry
consumer goods
cold war

1. A _____ is an industry that makes clothing and other _____

—things people buy; a _____ makes machinery, mining equipment, and weapons.

2. The _____ was a conflict between the United States and the Soviet Union

for power, whereas _____ was a policy of openness between the countries
supported by the Soviet Union.

3. A _____ was a powerful ruler of early Russia, while a _____
had no power and no land.

4. A _____ is an economic system under government control, while in a

_____ people own and control their own businesses.

5. Government can be an authoritarian political system such as _____, or a
representative form, such as democracy.

6. In Siberia's far north, you will find the cold, treeless plains known as _____,

with _____—soil that remains frozen all year; to the south, you will find a

region of forests known as the _____ .

7. A country can have people with mainly one heritage or be composed of groups of people with

different heritages; each group is called an _____ .

Copyright © by Glencoe/McGraw-Hill.

CHAPTER **15** Vocabulary Activity

vo•cab•u•lar•y vo-'kab-y
1: a list or collection of wor
alphabetically arranged

The Independent Republics: Words to Know

DIRECTIONS: Word Puzzle The alphabetical list contains the letters for spelling the words that answer the questions below. Write the word to answer each question, and cross out the letters used to spell the word. After you complete the questions, you will have used all but three letters. Write the three letters in the blanks for question 8 and then write what the letters stand for.

steppe   food processing   oasis
nature preserve   nomad   ethnic group
fault

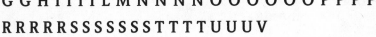

A A A A C C C D D E E E E E E E F F
G G H I I I I L M N N N N O O O O O O P P P P
R R R R R S S S S S S S S T T T T U U U V

1. The factory bought fresh produce from local farmers and made it into canned soup. What was the main job of the factory? _____

2. With a small herd of goats, the man traveled across the land, setting up a tent where he found food for the goats. What was the man? _____

3. A vast plain is called a prairie in the United States and Canada. In South America, it may be called *llanos* or the Pampas. What is another name for a vast treeless plain? _____

4. Today, countries set aside and protect some land. They make laws to prevent any development on the land. What is this area then called? _____

5. Most of the desert is dry, shifting sand. But here, green palms and rushes grow. What is this place called? _____

6. Land that sits across openings in the earth's crust often has earthquakes. What is a break in the earth's crust called? _____

7. Many countries have within their borders people who share a common heritage, race, or cultural background. They are members of an _____

8. ____ ____ ____ : _____

CHAPTER 16 Vocabulary Activity

vo•cab•u•lar•y vo-'kab-y
1: a list or collection of wo
alphabetically arranged

Southwest Asia: Words to Know

DIRECTIONS: Fill in the Blanks Select a term to fill each blank

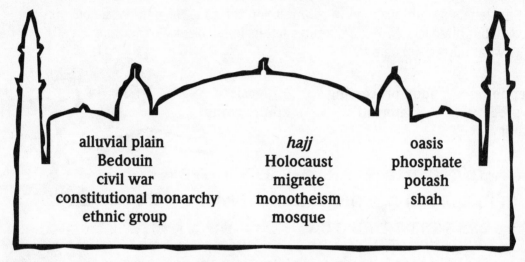

alluvial plain
Bedouin
civil war
constitutional monarchy
ethnic group

hajj
Holocaust
migrate
monotheism
mosque

oasis
phosphate
potash
shah

I had decided to (**1**)_____ to the city to find work. From my room, I could see the nearby (**2**)_____ where Muslims worship. Muslims practice (**3**)_____ , the worship of one god.

Mining is done in Israel. Near the Dead Sea, workers mine a mineral salt called (**4**)_____. Near Negev, (**5**)_____ is mined for making fertilizer.

Many victims of war are innocent people. In World War II, millions of Jews were killed in the (**6**)_____. In a war within a country, or (**7**)_____, ordinary citizens may be killed because they belong to an

opposing (**8**)_____.

Abdul knew it was time to make a (**9**)_____ to Makkah. It would be a long trip. Between the Tigris and Euphrates rivers, Abdul crossed the wide (**10**)_____ formed from flooding. In the desert, he stopped for water at each (**11**)_____. He met people called (**12**)_____ who wander the desert.

Governments vary. A country can be governed by a king or, as in Iran, by a (**13**)_____. Like Jordan, a country can be a (**14**)_____ in which a monarch shares power with elected officials.

Name_____ Date _____ Class _____

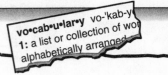

vo•cab•u•lar•y vo-'kab-y
1: a list or collection of wor
alphabetically arranged

North Africa: Words to Know

DIRECTIONS: Crossword Puzzle Complete the crossword puzzle by spelling out the terms called for in the clues.

silt	delta	hydroelectric power
consumer goods	*fellahin*	bazaar
hieroglyph	dictatorship	erg
casbah		

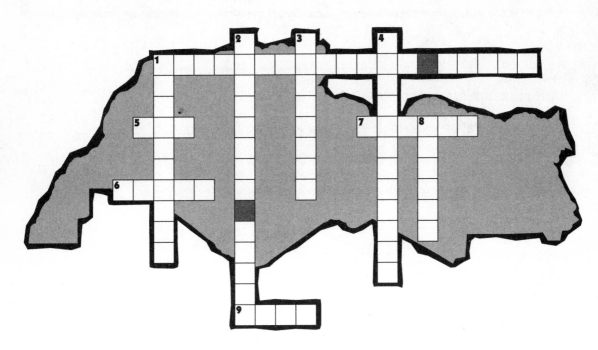

ACROSS

1. electric energy made from running water (two words)

5. a huge area of the Sahara with shifting sand dunes

6. a wide, triangle-shaped area of land at the mouth of a river, such as the Nile

7. an old area of Algiers with shops, mosques, and bazaars

9. particles of earth deposited by a river

DOWN

1. picture symbol used in ancient Egyptian writing

2. things people buy, such as household goods, clothing, shoes (two words)

3. the name given to most rural Egyptian farmers

4. government under one all-powerful ruler, such as Muammar al-Qaddhafi in Libya

8. a marketplace, such as in Egyptian towns

 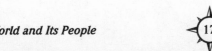

Name_____ Date _____ Class _____

CHAPTER 18 Vocabulary Activity

vo•cab•u•lar•y vo-'kab-y
1: a list or collection of wor
alphabetically arranged

West Africa: Words to Know

DIRECTIONS: Select a term to answer each question below. Write the correct word on the line.

mangrove	compound	*cataract*
savanna	drought	*land*
harmattan	desertification	*locked*
cacao	cassava	
ethnic group	bauxite	

3I d4

4. 6. **1.** What is an extreme shortage of water? _____

3. I. **2.** What is the plant from which chocolate is made? _____

8. 7. **3.** What is a dry wind that blows south from the Sahara in winter? _____

I. 2. **4.** What term means a group of people who share a culture, language, and traditions? _____

7. 8. **5.** What is a tropical tree that has roots growing above and beneath the water? _____

2. 3. **6.** What is a tropical grassland? _____

5. 10. **7.** What is the process of changing useful land into desert? _____

10. 4. **8.** What is a plant root used to make flour for bread? _____

6. II. **9.** What is a mineral resource used for making aluminum? _____

I. 5. **10.** What is an area of homes surrounded by walls? _____

12. 9. Name for waterfalls in Africa.

9. 12. Surrounded by other countries. not on the coast.

Copyright © by Glencoe/McGraw-Hill

Geography: The World and Its People

CHAPTER 19 Vocabulary Activity

vo•cab•u•lar•y vo-'kab-y
1: a list or collection of wor
alphabetically arranged

Central Africa: Words to Know

DIRECTIONS: Crossword Puzzle Decide which term is defined by each of the four clues below. Write the correct term in the circle, beginning with Box 1 for Question 1 and proceeding around the circle. Then follow the instructions to fill in the squares at the bottom of the page.

| canopy | hydroelectricity | basin | tsetse fly |

CLUES:

1. a broad, flat valley

2. a type of insect whose bite causes sleeping sickness in cattle and can infect humans

3. an umbrella-like forest covering, such as found in the rain forests of Zaire

4. electricity created by running water

DIRECTIONS: In each numbered box below, write the letter from the circle above that has the same number as the box. The term will name something Zaire, Gabon, Central African Republic, Cameroon, Congo, Equatorial Guinea, and São Tomé and Príncipe share.

29	11	5	30	31	16	13		2	12	24	4	15	16

CHAPTER 20 Vocabulary Activity

vo•cab•u•lar•y vo-'kab-y
1: a list or collection of wo
alphabetically arranged

East Africa: Words to Know

DIRECTIONS: Complete the crossword puzzle by spelling out the terms called for in the clues.

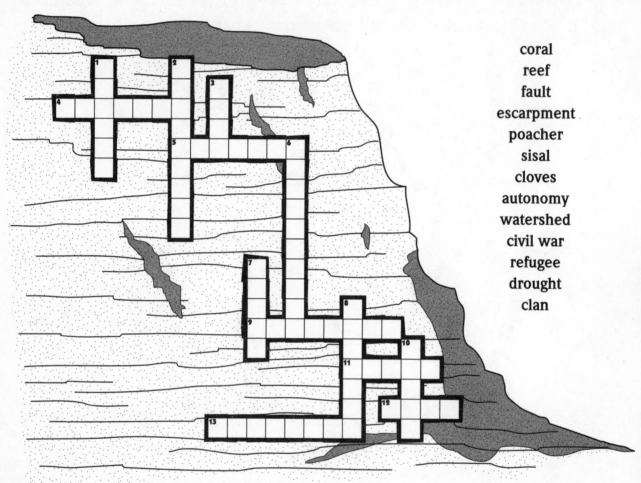

coral
reef
fault
escarpment
poacher
sisal
cloves
autonomy
watershed
civil war
refugee
drought
clan

ACROSS

4. a long, dry period
5. a person forced to flee a country for safety
9. self-government
11. hard, rocky material made of skeletons of sea animals
12. a group of related people
13. fighting between people of the same country

DOWN

1. a spice grown on Zanzibar
2. a ridge that sets the direction in which the waters of an area flow
3. a narrow ridge of coral, rock, or sand at or near the water's surface
6. a steep cliff
7. plant fiber used to make ropes and twine
8. a person who hunts and kills animals against the law
10. a crack in the earth's crust

CHAPTER 21 Vocabulary Activity

vo•cab•u•lar•y vo-'kab-y
1: a list or collection of wor
alphabetically arranged

South Africa and Its Neighbors: Words to Know

DIRECTIONS: Write the term from the box that matches each definition.

enclave
high veld
escarpment
slash-and-burn farming
apartheid
township
exclave
copper belt
sorghum

1. Neighborhood outside of a city, such as found in South Africa _____

2. A process in which the land is prepared by cutting trees and burning vegetation _____

3. A tall grass crop with seeds like corn _____

4. A small country within another country _____

5. Practices that separated South Africans belonging to different ethnic groups _____

6. A small area of a country separated from the main part of the country _____

7. A large area of copper mines, such as the region found in Zambia _____

8. Grass-covered, level plains in the center of South Africa _____

9. A steep cliff or slope dividing high and low ground _____

CHAPTER 22 Vocabulary Activity

vo•cab•u•lar•y vo-'kab-y
1: a list or collection of wo
alphabetically arranged

South Asia: Words to Know

DIRECTIONS: Select a term from the box to fill each blank in the paragraphs below.

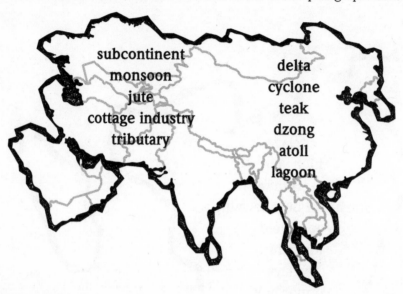

subcontinent
monsoon
jute
cottage industry
tributary

delta
cyclone
teak
dzong
atoll
lagoon

People in India do many jobs. Some are farmers who grow crops such as tea, sugarcane, and cotton. Another important crop is (**1**)_____ , the fiber used in making rope. Some Indian people may work in a factory, while others operate a (**2**)_____ _____ in their village, making beautiful silk or cotton cloth.

South Asia is called a (**3**)_____ because it is a landmass like a continent, only smaller. Seasons in South Asia are affected by (**4**)_____ winds that bring dry air part of the year and moist air another part. During summer monsoons, an intense storm called a (**5**)_____ may cause damage with high winds and heavy rains.

A river trek from source to sea is interesting. We began far upstream, at a small (**6**)_____ that led quickly into a larger river. We passed forests that provide (**7**)_____ , a wood used for building ships and making furniture. We arrived at the (**8**)_____ , which is fertile land formed by mud and sand at the mouth of the river. As we gazed out at the ocean, we could see a low-lying coral island, called an (**9**)_____ . This type of island circles a peaceful pool of water, or a (**10**)_____ .

High in the Himalayas, Bhutan's people follow the Buddhist religion. If you visit the mountains, you may see a (**11**) _____, a Buddhist center of prayer and study. These centers have shaped Bhutan's art and culture.

CHAPTER 23 Vocabulary Activity

vo•cab•u•lar•y vo-'kab-y
1: a list or collection of wo
alphabetically arranged

China: Words to Know

DIRECTIONS: Fill in the puzzle by spelling out the terms called for in the 12 clues. Then complete term 13, spelled vertically, and write its definition on line 13.

high-technology industries
consumer goods
terraced field
calligraphy
tungsten

loess
dike
typhoon
invest

dynasty
pagoda
empire
yurt

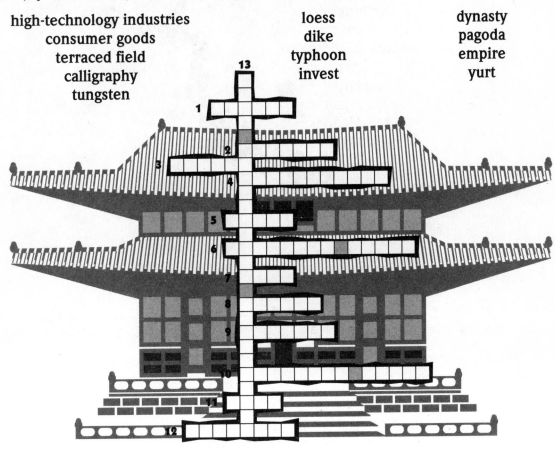

1. a many-storied, traditional Buddhist tower
2. a tropical storm with high winds and heavy rain, like an Atlantic hurricane
3. a group of territories under one ruler
4. the art of beautiful writing, as practiced in China
5. yellowish gray, fertile soil deposited by wind and water
6. products people use, such as cars, televisions, clothes, motorcycles
7. a round tent of animal skin used by nomadic herders
8. to put money into something for a later profit
9. a ruling family of early China
10. a farming area with steps of land cut into a hillside
11. a high bank of soil to prevent overflowing
12. a metal, found in China, used in electrical equipment

13. _____

CHAPTER 24 Vocabulary Activity

vo•cab•u•lar•y vo-'kab-y
1: a list or collection of wo
alphabetically arranged

Japan and the Koreas: Words to Know

DIRECTIONS: Select a term from the box to fill each blank in the paragraphs below.

archipelago
tsunami
intensive cultivation
clan
samurai
shogun
megalopolis
anthracite

A Japanese person today may trace ancestry to a (**1**) _____, or group of related families, that lived and ruled in Japan more than 1,500 years ago. Another later ancestor may have

lived in the 1200s and been a warrior, or (**2**) _____, serving a strong leader

called the (**3**) _____ .

When an earthquake occurs in the Pacific, it may create a huge sea wave called a

(**4**) _____ . This wave is especially dangerous to people who live near coasts, on

isolated islands, or on a chain of islands, which is called an (**5**) _____ . The destructive wave can wash away island towns and villages.

If you lived in Japan today, you might live in the (**6**) _____, or huge urban area including the capital city of Tokyo, as well as the cities of Yokohama, Osaka, and Nagoya. But even in this supercity, you might see crops planted between buildings or along highways. The Japanese,

with little land, practice (**7**) _____, using every bit of land to grow crops.

Though North Korea has more, minerals are important resources in both North and South Korea.

Both countries produce (**8**) _____, a hard type of coal. Both mine tungsten, which is used in electrical equipment.

CHAPTER 25 Vocabulary Activity

vo•cab•u•lar•y vo-'kab-y
1: a list or collection of wor
alphabetically arranged

Southeast Asia: Words to Know

DIRECTIONS: Write the terms in the blanks on the map to match the numbered descriptions given below.

alluvial plain   deforestation   delta   cassava   free port   abaca

1. This is a busy harbor where traders from many different countries stop. Here, goods can be loaded, stored, and shipped again without having to pay import taxes.
2. This region was formed from soil deposited by the river as it flowed down from the mountains. The river deposited rich soil that farmers use to grow crops.
3. This area, at the mouth of the river, is formed by soil deposits made as the river flows into the ocean. The soil here is fertile.
4. This area, at the edge of a rain forest, has been totally cut of all its trees.
5. This area is producing a plant fiber used to make rope.
6. In this area, farmers are growing a food crop. The root is used to make flour.

CHAPTER 26 Vocabulary Activity

vo·cab·u·lar·y vo-'kab-y
1: a list or collection of wo
alphabetically arranged

Australia and New Zealand: Words to Know

DIRECTIONS: Word Puzzle The alphabetical list contains the letters for spelling the words that answer the questions below. Write the words to answer the first eight questions and cross out the letters used to spell each word. You will have two remaining letters to help answer question 9.

coral	marsupial	fjord
outback	bush	geothermal power
station	*manuka*	

A A A A A A A A B B C C D E E E F G H H H I I J K K L L L M M M
N N O O O O O O P P R R R R R S S S S S T T T T U U U U W

1. The Great Barrier Reef is made up of a rocklike material from the skeletons of small sea animals. What is the material called? _____

2. Hydroelectric power is energy from moving water. What is energy from natural steam called?

_____

3. The Central Lowlands of Australia are partly dry grasslands. What are this and other inland regions of Australia called? _____

4. Rural areas in the United States may be called the countryside. What are rural areas called in Australia? _____

5. In the United States, ranchers operate ranches. What is a sheep and livestock ranch called in Australia? _____

6. A small shrub grows on the volcanic soil of New Zealand's North Island. What is its name?

_____

7. A type of Australian mammal carries its young in a pouch. What is this mammal called?

_____

8. On the southwest coast of New Zealand's South Island are long narrow fingers of the sea. What is this type of inlet called? _____

9. Write the two extra letters, starting with the last one first: ____ ____. The letters abbreviate a region in which Australia and New Zealand are located. Write that region's name:

_____

CHAPTER 27 Vocabulary Activity

vo•cab•u•lar•y vo-'kab-y
1: a list or collection of wo
alphabetically arranged

Oceania and Antarctica: Words to Know

DIRECTIONS: Matching Select a term from below to match each definition in the following groups.

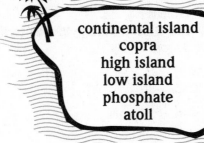

continental island
copra
high island
low island
phosphate
atoll

trust territory
rookery
crevasse
ice shelf
krill
ozone

Islands

1. A particular kind of low island that is a ring-shaped coral reef surrounding a bay

_____

2. An island either broken away from a continent or separated from it by rising water

_____

3. An island formed from coral _____

4. An island formed from volcanic activity centuries ago _____

Products

5. Dried coconut meat _____

6. A chemical used in fertilizers _____

Research

7. A form of oxygen in the atmosphere _____

8. A tiny shrimplike animal _____

9. Place where penguins make their nests _____

Antarctic Ice

10. A deep crack in the ice _____

11. Thick floating ice sheet connected to a coast _____

Government

12. A region under temporary control of the United States after World War II _____

Vocabulary Activities Answer Key

Chapter 1
Looking at the Earth: Words to Know
1. absolute location, relative location, place, environment, movement, region
2. hemisphere, latitude, longitude, grid system
3. galaxy, solar system
4. core, mantle, crust, magma
5. landform, continent, plateau, isthmus, peninsula
6. strait
7. plate tectonics, fault, earthquake, tsunami
8. orbit, revolution, axis, solstice, equinox
9. leap year
10. weathering, erosion
11. atmosphere
12. geography

Chapter 2
Water, Climate, and Vegetation: Words to Know
1. tropics, rain forest, savanna
2. current
3. marine west coast climate, Mediterranean climate, humid continental climate, humid subtropical climate
4. water cycle, evaporation, water vapor, condensation, precipitation
5. groundwater, aquifer
6. Weather, climate

Chapter 3
The World's People: Words to Know
1. language family
2. free enterprise
3. standard of living
4. emigrate
5. literacy rate
6. population density
7. culture
8. refugee
9. civilization
10. nonrenewable resource

11. socialism
12. renewable resource
13. cultural diffusion
14. natural resource

Chapter 4
The United States: Words to Know
Across
1. contiguous
2. farm belt
5. revolution
6. dry farming
9. national park
10. service industry
11. free enterprise system
12. acid rain
14. republic
16. immigrant
17. ethnic group

Down
1. coral reef
3. megalopolis
4. urban
7. multicultural
8. interdependent
13. mobile
14. rural
15. colony

Chapter 5
Canada: Words to Know
1. fossil fuel
2. parliamentary democracy
3. bilingual
4. prairie
5. prime minister
6. cordillera
7. newsprint
8. NAFTA

Vocabulary Activities Answer Key

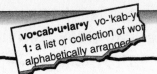

Chapter 6
Mexico: Words to Know
1. peninsula
2. subsistence farming
3. *mestizo*
4. service industry
5. smog
6. plantation
7. altitude
8. land bridge
9. *maquiladora*
10. industrialized
11. adobe
12. latitude
13. basins
14. colony

Chapter 7
Central America and the West Indies: Words to Know
1. bauxite
2. literacy rate
3. communism, cooperative
4. hurricane
5. plantation
6. nutrient
7. chicle
8. ladino
9. commonwealth, colony
10. isthmus, archipelago
11. dialect
12. light industry

Chapter 8
Brazil and Its Neighbors: Words to Know
Across
4. basin
6. escarpment
7. cassava
10. *llanos*
11. hydroelectric
12. *caudillo*
13. buffer

Down
1. *favela*
2. welfare
3. *selva*
5. altitude

8. sisal
9. *gaucho*
10. landlocked

Chapter 9
The Andean Countries: Words to Know
1. *campesinos*
2. cash crop
3. *quinoa*
4. sodium nitrate
5. *llanos*
6. cordillera
7. *estancia*
8. *gaucho*
9. tannin
10. altiplano
11. navigable
12. empire

Chapter 10
The British Isles and Scandinavia: Words to Know
1. loch
2. parliamentary democracy
3. peat
4. moor
5. welfare state
6. bog
7. geyser
8. constitutional monarchy
9. fjord

Chapter 11
Northwestern Europe: Words to Know
1. communism
2. Holocaust
3. navigable
4. acid rain
5. *autobahn*
6. polder
7. neutrality
8. watershed
9. loess
10. dialect
11. republic
12. multinational firm—a company that does business in several countries

Vocabulary Activities Answer Key

vo•cab•u•lar•y vo-'kab-y
1: a list or collection of wo
alphabetically arranged

Chapter 12
Southern Europe: Words to Know
1. service industry
2. suburb
3. mainland
4. emigrate
5. elevation
6. sirocco
7. city-state
8. dialect
9. plateau
10. textile

Chapter 13
Eastern Europe: Words to Know
1. communism
2. consumer goods
3. service industry
4. mosque
5. pope
6. invest
7. nature preserve
8. bog
9. oil shale

Chapter 14
Russia: Words to Know
1. light industry, consumer goods, heavy industry
2. cold war, *glasnost*
3. czar, serf
4. command economy, free enterprise system
5. communism
6. tundra, permafrost, taiga
7. ethnic group

Chapter 15
The Independent Republics: Words to Know
1. food processing
2. nomad
3. steppe
4. nature preserve
5. oasis
6. fault
7. ethnic group
8. CIS—Commonwealth of Independent States

Chapter 16
Words to Know
1. migrate
2. mosque
3. monotheism
4. potash
5. phosphate
6. Holocaust
7. civil war
8. ethnic group
9. *hajj*
10. alluvial plain
11. oasis
12. Bedouins
13. shah
14. constitutional monarchy

Chapter 17
North Africa: Words to Know
Across
1. hydroelectric power
5. erg
6. delta
7. *casbah*
9. silt

Down
1. hieroglyph
2. consumer goods
3. *fellahin*
4. dictatorship
8. bazaar

Chapter 18
West Africa: Words to Know
1. drought
2. cacao
3. harmattan
4. ethnic group
5. mangrove
6. savanna
7. desertification
8. cassava
9. bauxite
10. compound

Vocabulary Activities Answer Key

vo•cab•u•lar•y vo-'kab-y
1: a list or collection of wor
alphabetically arrang

Chapter 19
Central Africa: Words to Know
1. basin
2. tsetse fly
3. canopy
4. hydroelectricity
5. Central Africa

Chapter 20
East Africa: Words to Know
Across
4. drought
5. refugee
9. autonomy
11. coral
12. clan
13. civil war

Down
1. cloves
2. watershed
3. reef
6. escarpment
7. sisal
8. poacher
10. fault

Chapter 21
South Africa and Its Neighbors: Words to Know
1. township
2. slash-and-burn farming
3. sorghum
4. enclave
5. apartheid
6. exclave
7. copper belt
8. high veld
9. escarpment

Chapter 22
South Asia: Words to Know
1. jute
2. cottage industry
3. subcontinent
4. monsoon
5. cyclone
6. tributary

7. teak
8. delta
9. atoll
10. lagoon
11. dzong

Chapter 23
China: Words to Know
1. pagoda
2. typhoon
3. empire
4. calligraphy
5. loess
6. consumer goods
7. yurt
8. invest
9. dynasty
10. terraced field
11. dike
12. tungsten
13. high technology industries—industries that produce computers and other kinds of electronic equipment.

Chapter 24
Japan and the Koreas: Words to Know
1. clan
2. samurai
3. shogun
4. tsunami
5. archipelago
6. megaloplis
7. intensive cultivation
8. anthracite

Chapter 25
Southeast Asia: Words to Know
1. free port
2. alluvial plain
3. delta
4. deforestation
5. abaca
6. cassava

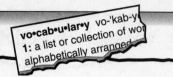

Chapter 26
Australia and New Zealand: Words to Know
1. coral
2. geothermal power
3. outback
4. bush
5. station
6. *manuka*
7. marsupial
8. fjord
9. S. H. Southern Hemisphere

Chapter 27
Oceania and Anarctica: Words to Know
1. atoll
2. continental island
3. low island
4. high island
5. copra
6. phosphate
7. ozone
8. krill
9. rookery
10. crevasse
11. ice shelf
12. trust territory

vo•cab•u•lar•y vo-'kab-y
1: a list or collection of wo
alphabetically arranged

Vocabulary Activities Notes

vo•cab•u•lar•y vo-'kab-y
1: a list or collection of wor
alphabetically arranged

vo•cab•u•lar•y vo-'kab-y
1: a list or collection of wo
alphabetically arranged

vo•cab•u•lar•y vo-'kab-y
1: a list or collection of wor
alphabetically arranged